For Henny Oey

First Book of Descant Recorder Solos

for descant (soprano) recorder and piano

by

WALTER BERGMANN

Faber Music Limited

London

7·95

© 1980 by Faber Music Ltd
First published in 1980 by Faber Music Ltd
3 Queen Square London WC1N 3AU
Cover design by Shirley Tucker
Printed in England by Caligraving Ltd

ISBN 0-571-50587-2

To buy Faber Music publications or to find out about the full range of titles available
please contact your local music retailer or Faber Music sales enquiries:

Faber Music Ltd, Burnt Mill, Elizabeth Way, Harlow, CM20 2HX England
Tel: +44 (0)1279 82 89 82   Fax: +44 (0)1279 82 89 83
sales@fabermusic.com   www.fabermusic.com

Preface

These pieces offer—in progressive order—an introduction to the world of music-making as well as to the basic technique of the descant (soprano) recorder. They are expressly designed for the true beginner on the instrument; the piano accompaniments are also simple enough for a student player. Short footnotes offer some technical and musical advice, and the recorder part also includes charts for both standard fingering and trill (shake) fingering.

The accompanying pianist is advised to study the piano part beforehand, and to keep a balance with the recorder player, i.e. to *accompany* and not to lead.

All the pieces are edited, arranged or, if not stated otherwise, composed by me.

WALTER BERGMANN

Contents

1. A Song

2. Berceuse

French traditional

3. Miniature March

4. Waltz

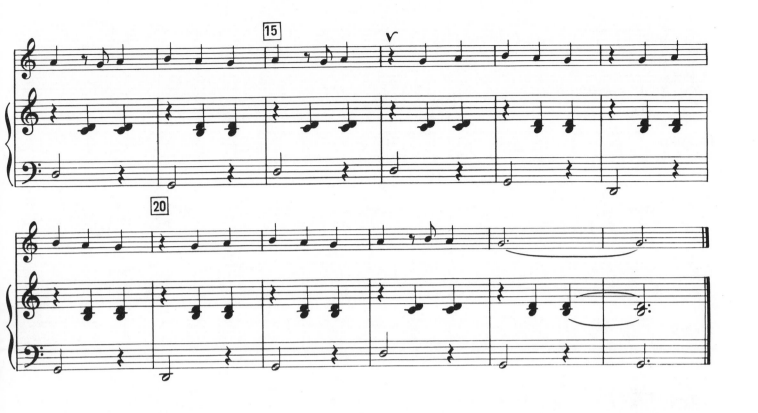

5. Scottish Air

4

6. Pony Trot

7. A la Claire Fontaine

French traditional

8. The Passion Chorale

Old German

9. Austrian Ländler

10. Old German Christmas Song

11. La Volta

Old English

12. Folk Tune

13. Les Bouffons

from Arbeau's *Orchésographie* (1589)

14. Gavotte

G. F. HANDEL
(1685–1759)

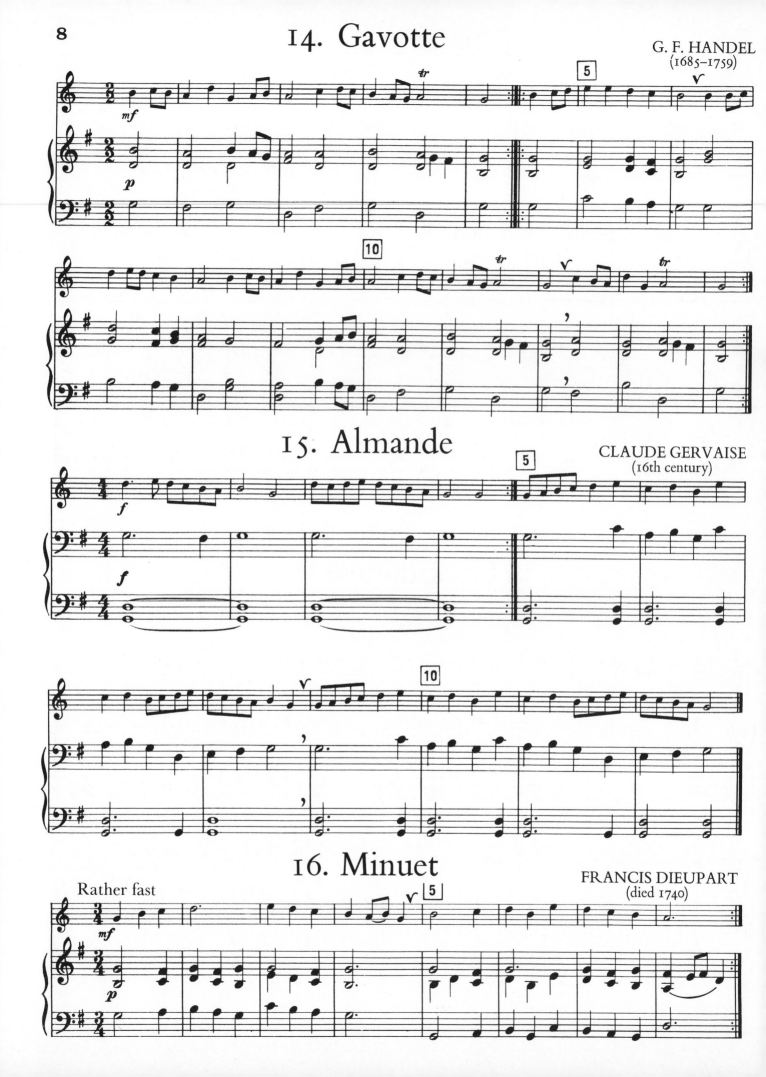

15. Almande

CLAUDE GERVAISE
(16th century)

16. Minuet

FRANCIS DIEUPART
(died 1740)

Rather fast

17. Polka

MM ♩ = approx. 88

Czech traditional

18. Variations on 'Lavender's Blue'

19. A Christmas Song: 'O Jesulein süss'

J. S. BACH
(1685–1750)

20. Babiole

J. J. NAUDOT
(18th century)

21. Musette

E. P. CHÈDEVILLE
(1696–1762)

22. Italian Folk Song

23. Minuet

J. PAISIBLE
(c. 1650–1721)

24. Andante from Partita No. 1

G. PH. TELEMANN
(1681–1767)

25. Duet

26. Hornpipe

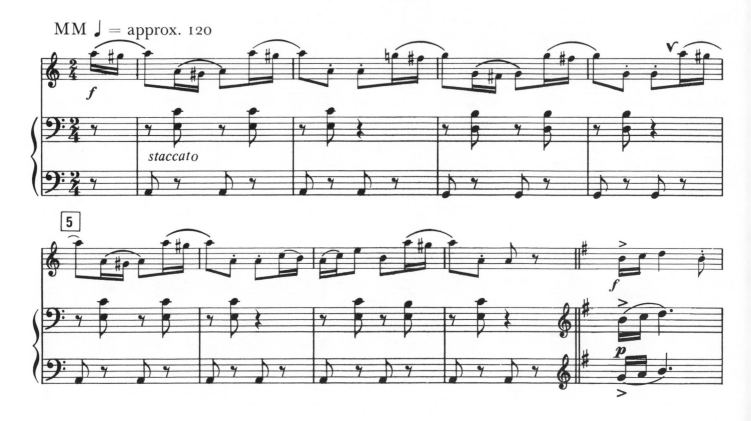

27. Norwegian Call

28. Gavotte

J. C. PEPUSCH
(1667–1752)

29. Grave

J. PAISIBLE
(c. 1650–1721)

30. Waltz Variations

BENJAMIN BRITTEN
(1913–1976)

Var. II

Var. III

More lively

31. Chaconne from 'The Fairy Queen'

HENRY PURCELL
(1659–1695)

Lively

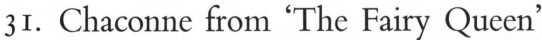

32. Canzonetta

CARL LOEWE
(1796–1869)

Footnotes

1. Play legato: reduce the gap between the notes to a minimum

3. Play staccato: the notes well detached.

5. Low notes need plenty of air but little breath pressure.

8. Chorales are the hymns of the German Protestant Church. This 'Passion' Chorale is best known through J. S. Bach's Church compositions, e.g. St. Matthew Passion.

13. *Bouffons* = comedians. With the accompaniment, this piece should give the effect of the 'pipe and tabor' (fife and drum).

14. The characteristic of the gavotte as a dance is its gracefulness. Handel wrote six sonatas for recorder with accompaniment and used the recorder in his chamber music and operas. This gavotte is the finale of one of his operas.

15. From a collection of Dances published by Pierre Attaignant in Paris in 1557. Tempo: one dance-step to a crotchet.

16. Francis Dieupart, whose first name is often mistakenly quoted as Charles, came to England in the first years of the 18th century. His harpsichord suites were known and admired by Bach. Dieupart composed six suites for recorder in 1705 and six sonatas for recorder in 1717.

17. The polka is a Czech dance of moderate speed ($\downarrow = c.$ 88).

20. *Babiole* = bauble. Naudot composed many works for 'musette [a small French bagpipe] or flûte à bec [recorder] or flûte traversière [flute] or oboe etc.' This is one of them. To achieve the rhythm indicated play the first note very slightly longer than its note value and the third note (the crotchet) as a quaver followed by a quaver rest.

21. A musette was both a French bagpipe and a dance-like piece of pastoral character. Like Naudot's 'Babiole' (No. 20) this 'Musette' was intended for a variety of musical instruments.

23. Paisible was a famous recorder player and a prolific composer for the instrument.

24. Play Andante (not Adagio) in $\frac{4}{4}$ (not $\frac{8}{8}$).

25. The piano part can be played on a second descant (soprano) recorder.

27. Play very slowly to create an atmosphere of complete tranquility.

28. Pepusch, a German emigrant to England, wrote sonatas and chamber music for the recorder, and arranged the music for John Gay's *Beggar's Opera* (1728). This 'Gavotte' is taken from one of his sonatas for treble recorder and figured bass.

30. This piece was written by Benjamin Britten for the piano before he was 12, and has been arranged (by permission of the composer) for descant recorder and piano. Britten, who played the recorder himself and was until his death President of the Society of Recorder Players in Great Britain, has used the recorder in several works including *Noyes Fludde, A Midsummer Night's Dream* and the *Alpine Suite* (for recorder trio).

32. This beautiful melody is composed for the voice and should be played accordingly. It has the greatest effect when played very slowly.